For Elizabeth
and with many thanks to Angie

First published in Great Britain in 1998 by National Trust (Enterprises) Ltd.
36 Queen Anne's Gate, London SW1H 9AS Registered Charity No. 205846

British Library Cataloguing in Publication Data
A catalogue record for this book is available from the British Library.
ISBN 0 7078 0259 8

Designed by Butterworth Design
Edited by Morwenna Wallis
Production by Bob Towell
Printed and Bound in China
Phoenix Offset

The National Trust ABC

Illustrated by

Ian Penney

The National Trust

Aa
Bb
Cc
Dd
Ee
Ff
Gg
Hh
Ii
Jj
Kk
Ll
Mm
Nn
Oo
Pp
Qq
Rr
Ss
Tt
Uu
Vv
Ww
Xx
Yy
Zz
Aa for apple

Bb for book

Cc Dd Ee Ff Gg Hh
Ii Jj Kk Ll Mm Nn Oo
Pp Qq Rr Ss Tt Uu
Vv Ww Xx Yy Zz Aa Bb
Cc for cat

Dd Ee Ff Gg Hh Ii
Jj Kk Ll Mm Nn Oo Pp
Qq Rr Ss Tt Uu Vv
Ww Xx Yy Zz Aa Bb Cc
Dd for duck

Ee Ff Gg Hh Ii Jj
Kk Ll Mm Nn Oo Pp Qq
Rr Ss Tt Uu Vv Ww
Xx Yy Zz Aa Bb Cc Dd

Ee for egg

Ff Gg Hh Ii Jj Kk
Ll Mm Nn Oo Pp Qq Rr
Ss Tt Uu Vv Ww Xx
Yy Zz Aa Bb Cc Dd Ee
Ff for frog

Gg Hh Ii Jj Kk Ll
Gg for goat

Hh
Ii
Jj
Kk
Ll
Mm
Nn
Oo
Pp
Qq
Rr
Ss
Tt
Uu
Vv
Ww
Xx
Yy
Zz
Aa
Bb
Cc
Dd
Ee
Ff
Gg
Hh for honey

Ii for insects

Jj Kk Ll Mm Nn Oo
Pp Qq Rr Ss Tt Uu Vv
Ww Xx Yy Zz Aa Bb
Cc Dd Ee Ff Gg Hh Ii
Jj for jack-in-a-box

Kk
Ll
Mm
Nn
Oo
Pp
Qq
Rr
Ss
Tt
Uu
Vv
Ww
Xx
Yy
Zz
Aa
Bb
Cc
Dd
Ee
Ff
Gg
Hh
Ii
Jj
SALT
Kk for kettle

Ll Mm Nn Oo Pp Qq
Rr Ss Tt Uu Vv Ww Xx
Yy Zz Aa Bb Cc Dd
Ee Ff Gg Hh Ii Jj Kk
Ll for ladder

Mm Nn Oo Pp Qq Rr
Ss Tt Uu Vv Ww Xx Yy
Zz Aa Bb Cc Dd Ee
Ff Gg Hh Ii Jj Kk Ll
Mm for mouse

Nn Oo Pp Qq Rr Ss
Tt Uu Vv Ww Xx Yy Zz
Aa Bb Cc Dd Ee Ff
Gg Hh Ii Jj Kk Ll Mm

Nn for nut

Oo
Nn
Mm
Ll
Kk
Jj
Ii
Hh
Gg
Ff
Ee
Dd
Cc
Oo for otter

and orange

Pp
Qq
Rr
Ss
Tt
Uu
Vv
Ww
Xx
Yy
Zz
Aa
Bb
Cc
Dd
Ee
Ff
Gg
Hh
Ii
Jj
Kk
Ll
Mm
Nn
Oo
Pp for pig

Qq
Rr
Ss
Tt
Uu
Vv
Ww
Xx
Yy
Zz
Aa
Bb
Cc
Dd
Ee
Ff
Gg
Hh
Ii
Jj
Kk
Ll
Mm
Nn
Oo
Pp
Qq for queen

Rr Ss Tt Uu Vv Ww
Xx Yy Zz Aa Bb Cc Dd
Ee Ff Gg Hh Ii Jj
Kk Ll Mm Nn Oo Pp Qq
Rr for roses

Ss
Tt
Uu
Vv
Ww
Xx
Yy
Zz
Aa
Bb
Cc
Dd
Ee
Ff
Gg
Hh
Ii
Jj
Kk
Ll
Mm
Nn
Oo
Pp
Qq
Rr
Ss for sandcastle

Tt
Uu
Vv
Ww
Xx
Yy
Zz
Aa
Bb
Cc
Dd
Ee
Ff
Gg
Hh
Ii
Jj
Kk
Ll
Mm
Nn
Oo
Pp
Qq
Rr
Ss
TEA
Tt for tortoise

Uu Vv Ww Xx Yy Zz
Aa Bb Cc Dd Ee Ff Gg
Hh Ii Jj Kk Ll Mm
Nn Oo Pp Qq Rr Ss Tt
Uu for umbrella

Vv for vegetables

Ww
Xx
Yy
Zz
Aa
Bb
Cc
Dd
Ee
Ff
Gg
Hh
Ii
Jj
Kk
Ll
Mm
Nn
Oo
Pp
Qq
Rr
Ss
Tt
Uu
Vv
Ww for web

Xx Yy Zz Aa Bb Cc
Dd Ee Ff Gg Hh Ii Jj
Kk Ll Mm Nn Oo Pp
Qq Rr Ss Tt Uu Vv Ww
DELIVERY
Xx as in Fox

Yy
Zz
Aa
Bb
Cc
Dd
Ee
Ff
Gg
Hh
Ii
Jj
Kk
Ll
Mm
Nn
Oo
Pp
Qq
Rr
Ss
Tt
Uu
Vv
Ww
Xx
Yy for yo-yo

Zz
Aa
Bb
Cc
Dd
Ee
Ff
Gg
Hh
Ii
Jj
Kk
Ll
Mm
Nn
Oo
Pp
Qq
Rr
Ss
Tt
Uu
Vv
Ww
Xx
Yy
Zz for zoetrope

Property Information

Fountains Abbey, North Yorkshire
Fountains Abbey was founded in 1132 by a group of Cistercian monks who broke away from their community in York to lead a simple and austere life in what was then a wild and isolated site. The community was thriving by the time the abbey was dissolved in 1539, and the ruins that remain show how impressive the monastery had become.

Coggeshall Grange Barn, Essex
Coggeshall is the oldest surviving timber-framed barn in Britain. It dates from 1140, and was originally used to store the crops of the Savigniac order of monks.

Bodiam Castle, East Sussex
Bodiam Castle was built in 1385 to protect against French raids on the south coast of England during the Hundred Years War. The ruins that remain today show that the castle was not only a military building but also a comfortable dwelling for a nobleman.

Dairy at Uppark, West Sussex
The Dairy at Uppark was built in a separate pavilion in the early nineteenth century by the landscape designer Humphry Repton. Here Sir Harry Fetherstonhaugh, who owned the house at this time, courted the young dairymaid, Mary Ann Bullock, and made her his bride.

Penrhyn Steam Engine, Gwynedd
Penrhyn is a vast nineteenth-century castle built in the Norman style with dramatic views of Snowdonia. It houses a number of interesting collections, including a museum of industrial locomotives.

Fountain at Cliveden, Buckinghamshire
The grand estate of Cliveden with its dramatic views over the River Thames was bought in 1893 by the wealthy American, William Astor. It was Astor who introduced much of the statuary into the gardens, including Thomas Waldo Story's spectacular Fountain of Love, which stands on the approach drive to the house.

Garden at Cotehele, Cornwall
Cotehele, a fine example of a Tudor courtyard house, is built on the banks of the River Tamar on the Devon/Cornwall border. A series of formal gardens is laid out near the house, and a luxuriant valley garden runs all the way down to the river, sheltered on both sides by woodland.

Alfriston Clergy House, East Sussex
The Clergy House at Alfriston is a timber-framed building situated on the green of a leafy South Downs village. Built in about 1350 for a farmer, it became the home of the local vicar. It was the first building to be acquired by the National Trust in 1896.

Brownsea Island, Dorset
The island of Brownsea lies in the middle of Poole Harbour. The last private owner, Mrs Bonham Christie, lived here in seclusion from 1927 to 1961, ensuring that it became an oasis for wildlife.

Biddulph 'Jungle', Staffordshire
The 'world image' garden at Biddulph Grange was created by James and Maria Bateman in the mid-nineteenth century. In order to represent the different parts of the world and their varied climates in distinct areas of the garden, they introduced appropriate plants and trees for 'China', 'Egypt', the American Pinetum, and so on.

Kitchen at Castle Drogo, Devon
Castle Drogo was built by the architect Edwin Lutyens between 1910 and 1930 for Julius Drewe, who had made a fortune from the Home & Colonial grocery stores. Although Lutyens created a 'medieval' granite castle, the kitchen was provided with the most up-to-date furnishings and equipment.

Souter Lighthouse, South Tyneside
Built in 1870 just south of the Tyne estuary, Souter was the first lighthouse to be powered by an alternating electric current, and could be seen from as far as 19 miles out at sea.

Glendurgan Maze, Cornwall
This beautiful valley garden lying on the north side of the Helford river contains a number of exotic and tender plants which were imported in the early nineteenth century. The laurel maze, laid out in 1833, has recently been restored.

Erddig Nursery, Wrexham
Erddig, a late seventeenth-century house near Wrexham, is rich not only in furnishings but also in written records of the Yorke family, who inherited the estate in 1733, and – remarkably – of their servants. The nursery has been reconstructed to show how it may have looked at the beginning of the twentieth century using the toys of Simon and Philip Yorke, the last private owners of Erddig.

Westbury Orchard, Gloucestershire
A Dutch-style formal water garden laid out at the end of the seventeenth century, and the earliest of its kind surviving in either England or Holland. Restored in 1971, it has been planted with species of fruit trees – apples, pears and plums – dating from before 1700.

Blickling Pyramid, Norfolk
Blickling is a Jacobean house set in fine parkland. The estate buildings include a mausoleum in the shape of a pyramid, designed by Joseph Bonomi in 1796 to contain the remains of the 2nd Earl of Buckinghamshire and his two Countesses.

Tintagel Quilt, Cornwall
The Old Post Office at Tintagel is a fourteenth-century hall house of granite. Inside, it is furnished with traditional pieces, including bedsteads with patchwork coverlets. When the penny post was introduced in the nineteenth century, the house became a receiving office for the district.

River at Charlecote, Warwickshire
The present house was built in the 1550s, on the banks of the River Avon. Queen Elizabeth I was a visitor here, and the youthful William Shakespeare is said to have been caught poaching deer from the park.

Seashore at Old Harry Rocks, Dorset
At the eastern tip of the Purbeck Hills, sheer cliffs drop 500 feet to the sea below, where the remains of the chalk stacks called Old Harry Rocks are gradually crumbling away.

Rowallane Tower, Co. Down
In 1903 Hugh Armytage Moore inherited the house at Rowallane, with its walled garden and bell tower. From the unpromising thin and peaty soil, he produced a spectacular garden with particularly fine displays of rhododendrons and azaleas.

Underground passage at Petworth, West Sussex
There has been a great house at Petworth since the Middle Ages. As a fire precaution, the kitchen and servants quarters were accommodated in a separate block, built in the mid 18th-century, and food was taken to the dining room through a passage underneath the courtyard.

Lacock Village, Wiltshire
The charming village of Lacock was originally established for those working on the estates of the nearby Abbey in the thirteenth century, but grew prosperous from the wool industry which was so important to England's finances during the late Middle Ages.

Windmill at Wicken Fen, Cambridgeshire
One of the oldest and most important wetland nature reserves in the country, Wicken Fen is virtually all that remains of the once vast area of undrained fenland which covered 2,500 square miles from Lincolnshire to Suffolk.

Box Room at Calke Abbey, Derbyshire
The Harpur Crewe family, who built Calke Abbey in 1704, were great collectors who rarely threw anything away. When the National Trust took over the house in 1985, the house was stuffed with their belongings in startling disarray, particularly in Sir Vauncey's bedroom up in the attics.

Steam Yacht *Gondola*, Cumbria
The steam yacht *Gondola* was built in 1860 to take passengers from the railway terminus across Coniston Water to hotels on the opposite shore. Now fully returned to its Victorian splendour, it still plies the waters of the lake.

Killerton 'zoo', Devon
The costume collection now housed at Killerton was built up by the actress Paulise de Bush, who first began to amass historical items of dress for the Shakespearean plays that she staged. The collection is particularly rich in children's clothes, with accompanying games and toys; among them are Victorian examples of Noah's Ark and zoos.

Aa Bb Cc Dd Ee Ff Gg Hh Ii Jj Kk Ll Mm Nn Oo Pp
Kk Ll Mm Nn Oo Pp Qq Rr Ss Tt Uu Vv Ww Xx Yy
Tt Uu Vv Ww Xx Yy Zz Aa Bb Cc Dd Ee Ff Gg Hh Ii
Bb Cc Dd Ee Ff Gg Hh Ii Jj Kk Ll Mm Nn Oo Pp Qq
Ll Mm Nn Oo Pp Qq Rr Ss Tt Uu Vv Ww Xx Yy Zz
Uu Vv Ww Xx Yy Zz Aa Bb Cc Dd Ee Ff Gg Hh Ii Jj
Cc Dd Ee Ff Gg Hh Ii Jj Kk Ll Mm Nn Oo Pp Qq Rr Ss
Mm Nn Oo Pp Qq Rr Ss Tt Uu Vv Ww Xx Yy Zz Aa
Vv Ww Xx Yy Zz Aa Bb Cc Dd Ee Ff Gg Hh Ii Jj Kk
Dd Ee Ff Gg Hh Ii Jj Kk Ll Mm Nn Oo Pp Qq Rr Ss Tt
Nn Oo Pp Qq Rr Ss Tt Uu Vv Ww Xx Yy Zz Aa Bb
Ww Xx Yy Zz Aa Bb Cc Dd Ee Ff Gg Hh Ii Jj Kk Ll
Ee Ff Gg Hh Ii Jj Kk Ll Mm Nn Oo Pp Qq Rr Ss Tt Uu
Oo Pp Qq Rr Ss Tt Uu Vv Ww Xx Yy Zz Aa Bb Cc
Ww Xx Yy Zz Aa Bb Cc Dd Ee Ff Gg Hh Ii Jj Kk Ll
Ee Ff Gg Hh Ii Jj Kk Ll Mm Nn Oo Pp Qq Rr Ss Tt Uu
Oo Pp Qq Rr Ss Tt Uu Vv Ww Xx Yy Zz Aa Bb Cc
Ww Xx Yy Zz Aa Bb Cc Dd Ee Ff Gg Hh Ii Jj Kk Ll
Ee Ff Gg Hh Ii Jj Kk Ll Mm Nn Oo Pp Qq Rr Ss Tt Uu
Oo Pp Qq Rr Ss Tt Uu Vv Ww Xx Yy Zz Aa Bb Cc